STORYTIME

STORYTIME

stories from the
BIBLE

The story of RUTH

Once, during the days when the judges ruled over Israel, there was a great famine in the land of Canaan. To escape this scourge an Israelite named Elimelech travelled far from his own city of Bethlehem into the land of Moab, east of the Salt Sea. His wife and their two sons went with him and the family settled down in Moab and eventually his sons married women of Moab. Chilion married a girl called Orpah and Mahlon married a girl called Ruth.

Then great tragedy befell the family. Elimelech and his two sons died and Naomi was left a widow and childless in a strange land.

Naomi, having heard that the days of famine were over in Canaan, decided to return to her native land where, now that she had no family, she would at least be among her own friends.

She told her two daughters-in-law of her decision, saying, "Go you and return to the homes of your parents. I shall pray that the Lord will deal kindly with you always and that you may find lasting happiness with new husbands."

Orpah kissed Naomi and, bidding her farewell, went away to her own home.

But Ruth would not leave Naomi.

"Entreat me not to leave you," Ruth said. "For where you go there will I go, and where you live I will live. Your people shall be my people and your God shall be my God. Where you die I will die, and there will I be buried. Naught but death shall part thee and me."

Naomi was deeply moved by Ruth's devotion and was pleased to have the companionship of this girl who had been a good wife to her son during their short marriage.

Together they set out on their long journey and at last they reached the town of Bethlehem in the land of the Tribe of Judah.

They arrived at the beginning of the barley harvest, when the people were cutting their grain.

Now it was the custom in those ancient times to leave a certain amount of grain in the fields after each day's gleaning. This grain was intended for the poor, who were allowed to come and gather it up for themselves. This custom was in keeping with the Lord's command that His poor should always be fed.

So, as Ruth and Naomi were poor and since it was harvest time, Ruth said to Naomi, "Let me go into the fields for grain."

And Naomi answered, "Go, my daughter."

Then Ruth went with some other women to glean in the fields around Bethlehem. And it happened that the fields where Ruth went were owned by a very rich man named Boaz, a relative of Naomi's dead husband, Elimelech.

When Boaz visited the fields that day to see how the harvest was progressing he noticed Ruth and asked his men about the strange young woman.

One of his servants told him that the young woman was called Ruth and that she had travelled with Naomi out of the land of Moab.

Boaz then approached Ruth and spoke kindly to her. He told her not to go into any other man's field, for she could glean in his fields as long as she liked. When she was thirsty, he said, she should go to the pitchers which the young men had filled and drink what she wanted.

"But why should you be so kind to a stranger?" asked Ruth.

"I have heard of your devotion to your mother-in-law Naomi," Boaz explained, "and I know that you left your mother and father and the land of your birth. May the Lord God of this land of Israel reward you."

When all the reapers and gleaners rested for lunch at noon Boaz gave Ruth food to eat and he commanded his workers how to treat her. "Let fall some handfuls of grain for her that she may take them, and do not rebuke her."

Ruth gleaned in the fields until sundown and when she took the grain home to Naomi she also told her mother-in-law about the kindness of Boaz.

After that Ruth went every sunny day into the fields of Boaz and gleaned there until the end of the barley harvest and of the wheat harvest.

One day, when the harvest was nearly over, Naomi said to Ruth, "Tonight Boaz is going to winnow his grain. Go to his threshing floor and watch him and his people, and when Boaz lies down to sleep go quietly and lie at his feet and wait until he tells you what to do."

Ruth did as Naomi instructed her and she watched for hours as the reapers threw the grain, and the small broken pieces of straw which were left mixed with it after the threshing, up into the air while the wind was blowing. Then the wind would blow away the straw, which was light, but the grains of barley, being heavier, would fall down by themselves in a heap on the ground. This was how the grain was winnowed.

After winnowing there was a feast, and later, when Boaz slept, Ruth lay down silently at his feet.

It was after midnight when Boaz suddenly awoke and, seeing someone sleeping at his feet, he asked, "Who are you?"

"I am Ruth, your relative and your servant," the girl answered.

And Boaz, who was in love with Ruth but who had feared he was too old to win the girl's affection, answered, "May the Lord bless you, and I promise you now that I will take care of you for the rest of my life."

In those days the cities of Canaan had walls around them. At the gates in these walls the people used to meet and that was the place where the rulers came to hold their court and sentence those who disobeyed the law. People also bought and sold goods at the gates, making a kind of market there, and whoever came into the city or went out of it passed through the city gates. So that whenever any man wanted all the people to know of something he was going to do he would go and speak about it at the gates.

Now on the morning after the barley had been winnowed Boaz went to the gates of Bethlehem and sat down in a seat there. He called to him ten of the elders, or principal men, of the city and then Boaz spoke to them, and to all the people, and he told them that he was going to take Ruth, the daughter-in-law of Naomi, to be his wife.

"You are my witnesses," said Boaz. "You are the people to whom I tell it, that you may know it yourselves and also tell others."

"We are the witnesses," answered the people and the elders. "And may God bless Ruth and make her like Leah and Rachel."

So Ruth became the wife of Boaz and she bore him a son. Naomi took the child and became his nurse, and the child was a joy to her and he brought fame to Ruth and Boaz. For when he grew up he became the father of Jesse, who in turn became the father of David, the beloved King of Israel.

THE FIRST KING of ISRAEL

Samuel was a prophet and a man of God and under his inspired leadership the twelve tribes of Israel became a strong and united people.

But there came a time when the people began to desire an earthly ruler.

"Let us have a king to rule us, as the other nations have," they said to Samuel.

"You should have no other ruler but the Lord," said Samuel. "During these long four hundred years the people of Israel have bent their knees to no man. God is their king and so it should always be."

But the people were stubborn in their desire. "We want a king," they said.

Then Samuel warned the people. "A king will take your sons to be his charioteers and his horsemen, to till his land and reap his harvests. He will take your daughters to be his cooks and maidservants. Your fields he will take too, and your best vineyards and olive groves. He will take your best young men and your asses and put them to work for him. And the day will come when you will cry out against your king, but the Lord will not listen to you."

But the people refused to heed the warning of Samuel, only repeating obstinately, "We want a king."

God decided that they should have their will and He instructed Samuel that a young man called Saul of the tribe of Benjamin should become king of Israel.

And so, in the city of Mizpah, Samuel anointed Saul as the first king of Israel.

Then the people hailed Saul, crying, "God save the King!"

In the early days of his reign Saul obeyed the commandments of God and he became a great and a brave king. He led the Israelites against their enemies on the north and the south and the east, and against the Philistines who lived along the coast of southern Canaan. Under his leadership the Israelites were victorious in all these wars.

But then Saul grew proud and began to defy God's commands, and so God turned away from Saul.

"Because you reject the word of God," Samuel warned Saul, "the kingdom of Israel will be torn from your hands."

With this warning they parted, and the aged prophet and the king never met again.

David, Israel's greatest king

Samuel went to Bethlehem and on the Lord's instructions he anointed a young shepherd lad to be king of Israel after Saul. The boy's name was David and he was the son of Jesse. But David was not to be king at once, not until after the death of Saul.

Now when the spirit of the Lord came upon the boy David it departed from Saul and the king became sick with the thought of his sin. His soul became troubled and he became subject to periods of deep depression.

As he became more and more melancholy his servants tried every means to distract and amuse him. One of them had heard of David's skill as a singer, for the young shepherd was famous for the beautiful hymns that he composed on his harp. On this servant's suggestion the boy was summoned to the palace to amuse the melancholy king.

So it was that David, who had been chosen by God, came and stood before Saul, who had been rejected by God.

Saul came to love the handsome singer and appointed him his personal armour-bearer. David stayed constantly at Saul's side so that when the evil spirit came upon Saul, David took a harp and played upon the strings and Saul was refreshed and felt well again, for the evil spirit departed from him at the sound of the music.

Now during the years of Saul's kingship many of Israel's enemies had been vanquished and for some years the children of Israel had known peace.

But one day the Philistines again gathered together their armies to fight against Israel. Saul and the men of Israel made ready for the battle and they faced their enemy in the valley of Elah, in the lands of the Tribe of Judah.

The camp of the Philistines was on a mountain on one side of the valley while across the valley on another mountain stood the camp of the Israelites.

The Philistines had in their ranks a giant of a soldier whose name was Goliath of Gath. This man was over nine feet tall and he wore a coat of mail and a helmet of brass upon his head. He had brass plates on his legs so that no sword or spear might wound him, and his sword was so heavy that no other man could carry it.

Now as the two armies waited to see who would give the signal for the battle to start, Goliath came down into the valley between the two armies and challenged the Israelites.

"I defy your whole army," he shouted. "Choose one man from among you and let him come down and fight me. If he wins and kills me then my people shall be your servants. But if I win and kill him then the Israelites will bow down to the Philistines and be our slaves. Is there one among you brave enough to take up my challenge?"

When Saul heard these words he was dismayed. There was no man in all of Israel as tall and as powerful as Goliath of Gath. It would be an unequal fight. How could he, their king, ask any man to volunteer for such a contest?

But David, who had been tending a flock of sheep nearby, had also heard the giant's challenge, and now he approached the king. "I will fight Goliath," he said.

"You are but a youth," Saul protested, "and he has been a man of war all his life."

Then David told Saul how he had killed a lion and a bear with his bare hands when they had attacked his father's sheep. "The Lord who saved

me from the lion and the bear will save me from this Philistine," he said.

Then Saul said to David: "Go, and the Lord be with you. But take my own coat of armour, my sword and my helmet, and may they be a shield to you."

David tried on the suit of armour but promptly discarded it. He was not accustomed to swords and armour, as he was too young at this time to be in the army.

Then David, bending down, chose five smooth stones out of a brook and put them in a shepherd's bag which he carried with him. Armed only with his sling in one hand and his shepherd's staff in the other he went down into the valley to meet the giant.

When Goliath saw the slender shepherd boy, gentle-faced and unarmed, he was torn between astonishment and rage. "Am I a dog that you come to fight me with sticks?" he roared.

But David was unafraid. "You come to me trusting in your sword, your shield and your spear. But the God of Israel is my defender. In Him do I put my trust and He will deliver you to me this day so that everyone will know the strength of the Lord."

David walked towards Goliath until the shadow of the giant blotted out the sun from his view. Then taking a stone from his bag he put it into his sling and sent it flying towards the giant. It struck Goliath on the forehead, sinking deep into his brain and felling him to the ground like a dead tree.

So David overcame the Philistine with a sling and a stone, for there was no sword in his hand. The Israelites won a great battle against the Philistines that day in the Valley of Elah.

And, after many years had passed and when he was thirty-seven years of age, David, killer of Goliath and sweet singer of Israel, became Israel's greatest king.

STORYTIME